Collins

AQA GCSE 9-1 Revision

Design and Technology

Design and Technology

AQA
GCSE 9-1

Workbook

Paul Anderson and David Hills-Taylor

Contents

Tools, Equipment and Processes

New and Emerging Technologies

Design Strategies

1 The table shows three design strategies.

Complete the table by giving **one** advantage and **one** disadvantage of using each design strategy.

Design Approach	Advantage of Strategy	Disadvantage of Strategy
Iterative design		
User-centred design		
Systems thinking		

[6]

Total Marks _____ / 6

Electronic Systems

1. The table shows different electronic components.

Complete the table by stating whether each component is an input, process or output device and giving an example application of each in a product.

Component	Input, Process or Output	Application
Push switch		
Lamp		
Microcontroller		
Thermistor		
Buzzer		

[10]

Total Marks .... / 10

The Work of Others: Designers

1 Name a designer that you have studied.

.... [1]

2 State a product that the designer given in your answer to question 1 has designed.

.... [1]

3 Give **four** features of the design given in your answer to question 2.

1 ....

....

2 ....

....

3 ....

....

4 ....

.... [4]

Total Marks .... / 6

The Work of Others: Companies

1 Name a design company that you have studied.

.... [1]

2 State a product that the company given in your answer to question 1 has designed.

.... [1]

3 Give **four** features of the design given in your answer to question 2.

1 ....

....

2 ....

....

3 ....

....

4 ....

.... [4]

Total Marks .... / 6

Ecological, Environmental and Social Issues

1 Explain **three** ways that a product can be designed to be more sustainable.

1 ....

....

....

....

2 ....

....

....

....

3 ....

....

....

....

....

[6]

2 The image shows the Fairtrade Certification mark.

What is meant by the term 'fair trade'?

....

....

....

[2]

Total Marks .... / 8

Research and Investigation

1 Explain why designers conduct market research.

....

....

....

.... [2]

2 Explain the purpose of a focus group.

....

....

....

.... [2]

3 Give **two** types of data that can be used when investigating a design problem.

1 ....

2 .... [2]

4 Which of the following is the correct definition of anthropometric data? Tick one correct box.

   a Height measurements taken from a small sample of people. ☐

   b A range of body measurements taken from large numbers of people. ☐

   c A range of body measurements taken from a small sample of people. ☐

   d Head measurements taken from millions of people. ☐ [1]

Total Marks .... / 7

Briefs and Specifications

1 A design brief for a new product is shown.

> **Design brief**
>
> Young children learn about the world around them through play.
>
> A local company is designing an educational toy aimed at children aged 4–7.
> The toy must help the children to improve their literacy skills.

Write a **three**-point design specification for a product that would meet the design brief.

Explain why each point is important.

1 ....

....

Explanation ....

....

....

2 ....

....

Explanation ....

....

....

3 ....

....

Explanation ....

....

....

[6]

Total Marks .... / 6

Exploring and Developing Ideas

1 Sketching ideas can be one stage of an iterative design process.

Give **four** other possible stages of an iterative design process.

1 ....

2 ....

3 ....

4 .... [4]

2 The image shows a freehand sketch of a product idea.

Explain why designers produce freehand sketches of ideas for products.

....

....

....

....

....

....

....

  [4]

| Total Marks | / 8 |

Communication of Ideas 1

1 A company wants to design a toy car for small children. They have asked you to generate an idea for the design.

1.1) On the grid, produce an isometric drawing of your design idea. [4]

1.2) Annotate your design to indicate the main features, including:

- sizes

- the materials and finishes to be used

- how it could be made.

[6]

Total Marks .... / 10

1 In the space provided, produce a third-angle projection of the following component.

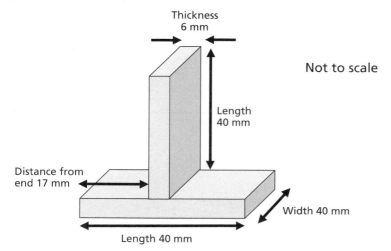

Thickness
6 mm

Not to scale

Length
40 mm

Distance from
end 17 mm

Width 40 mm

Length 40 mm

Include all sizes needed to allow manufacture of the component.

[11]

Total Marks _____ / 11

Computer-Based Tools

1 Complete the table by giving a suitable computer-based tool for completing each task listed.

Task	Computer-Based Tool
Creating a bill of materials for a product that is to be manufactured	
Creating a 3D model of a product	
Preparing images of a product prototype for inclusion in a face-to-face presentation	
Creating visual aids for presentation of a prototype at a focus group meeting	
Hosting a virtual meeting	

[5]

2 **2.1)** What type of software can be used for creating graphs?

[1]

2.2) What type of software can be used for viewing designs from different angles?

[1]

Total Marks _____ / 7

Prototype Development

1 Give **two** reasons why designers evaluate prototypes.

1 ....

....

2 ....

....

[2]

2 State **six** considerations that designers should take account of when developing prototypes of products or systems.

1 ....

....

2 ....

....

3 ....

....

4 ....

....

5 ....

....

6 ....

....

[6]

Total Marks .... / 8

1 The table shows different sources of energy.

Complete the table by stating whether each is renewable or non-renewable and describing how each is used to produce energy.

Source of Energy	Renewable or Non-Renewable	Description of How Energy is Produced
Nuclear power		
Solar energy		
Wind energy		

[9]

Total Marks .... / 9

Mechanical Systems 1

1 State which type of motion is represented by each of the following descriptions.

1.1) Swinging backwards and forwards

.... [1]

1.2) Moving straight in one direction

.... [1]

1.3) Moving in a circle

.... [1]

1.4) Moving backwards and forwards

.... [1]

2 A first-class lever is being used to raise a load of 60 N. The effort needed to move the load is 24 N.

Calculate how far the load was applied from the fulcrum (length A).

....

....

....

....

....

.... [4]

Mechanical Systems 2

1 Describe how the design of a cam can change the motion output from the follower attached to it.

_____

_____

_____

_____

_____

_____

_____

[4]

2 Two bevel gears similar to those shown are being used in a mechanical device.

Not to scale

The input gear has 48 teeth and rotates at a rate of 60 revolutions per minute (rpm).

If the output gear needs to rotate at a rate of 240 rpm, how may teeth does it need to have?

_____

_____

_____

_____

_____

[4]

Total Marks _____ / 8

Properties of Materials

1. State the meaning of the following properties.

   1.1) Toughness

   ....

   .... [1]

   1.2) Electrical conductivity

   ....

   .... [1]

   1.3) Elasticity

   ....

   .... [1]

2. Name the material property described by each of the following statements.

   2.1) The ability of a material for its shape to be permanently changed without the material breaking.

   .... [1]

   2.2) The ability of a material to be changed from a solid to a liquid by heat.

   .... [1]

   2.3) The ability of a material to draw in moisture, light or heat.

   .... [1]

3. Explain the difference between a physical property and a working property of a material.

   ....

   ....

   ....

   .... [2]

Total Marks .... / 8

Materials: Paper and Board

1 Explain the differences between duplex board and solid white board.

_____

_____

_____

_____

_____

_____

_____

_____

[4]

2 A manufacturer has to cut as many copies as possible of the following shape from a piece of foam board.

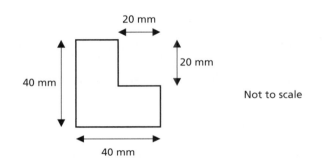

Not to scale

Sketching on the representation of the board shown here, show how you would lay out the shapes to minimise waste.

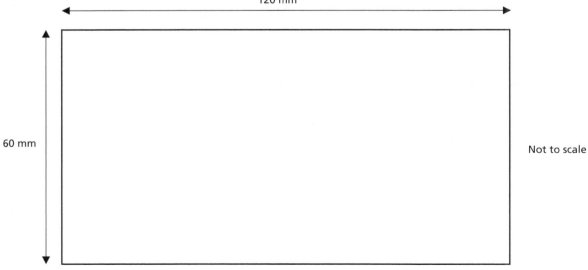

Not to scale

[2]

Materials: Timber

1 For each of the timber-based materials listed in the following table, state whether they are a hardwood, a softwood or a manufactured board, and list a typical application.

An example has been completed for you.

Material	Hardwood, Softwood or Manufactured Board?	Example of Typical Application
Ash	Hardwood	Tool handles
Larch	a)	b)
Mahogany	c)	d)
Plywood	e)	f)
Spruce	g)	h)
Balsa	i)	j)

[10]

2 Explain what is meant by 'seasoning' wood.

[3]

Materials: Metals

1 Name the metallic elements that are the major components of the following metal alloys.

1.1) Stainless steel

.... [2]

1.2) Brass

.... [2]

2 **2.1)** Name **four** stock forms in which metal is commonly available.

1 ....

2 ....

3 ....

4 .... [4]

2.2) Explain why a designer may modify a design so that a manufacturer can use metal in stock form.

....

....

....

....

....

.... [4]

3 What is the main difference between ferrous and non-ferrous metals?

....

.... [1]

Total Marks .... / 13

Materials: Polymers

1 Using notes and/or sketches, describe how thermoforming polymers are produced from their raw materials.

[4]

2 A manufacturer is producing solid plastic cubes. Each cube is 30 mm on each side. The manufacturer is using a polymer with a density of 960 kg m^{-3}.

Calculate the mass of material needed to make 10 000 cubes. Assume that no material is wasted during the process.

[5]

Total Marks _____ / 9

Materials: Textiles

1 **1.1)** Name a natural fibre that is used to make fabric.

_____ [1]

1.2) Give a typical use for this fabric.

_____ [1]

1.3) Explain why this fibre is an appropriate choice for this application.

_____

_____

_____

_____ [3]

2 **2.1)** Name a synthetic fibre that is used to make fabric.

_____ [1]

2.2) Give a typical use for this fabric.

_____ [1]

2.3) Explain why this fibre is an appropriate choice for this application.

_____

_____

_____

_____ [3]

Total Marks _____ / 10

New Materials

1 **1.1)** Explain what is meant by a 'smart material'.

....

....

....

.... [2]

1.2) Name a smart material.

.... [1]

1.3) Describe the properties of this material that make it 'smart'.

....

....

....

.... [2]

1.4) State an application for which this material is typically used.

.... [1]

2 **2.1)** Explain what is meant by a 'technical textile'.

....

.... [1]

2.2) Name a technical textile and give an application for which it is typically used.

....

....

....

.... [2]

Total Marks .... / 9

Standard Components

1 Name **two** standard components that are used with each of the following materials.

1.1) Paper

1 ....

2 .... [2]

1.2) Fabric

1 ....

2 .... [2]

1.3) Metal

1 ....

2 .... [2]

1.4) Timber

1 ....

2 .... [2]

2 Explain why a company may decide to use standard components in a product.

....

....

....

....

....

....

....

....

.... [5]

Total Marks .... / 13

Finishing Materials

1 The table shows different types of material.

Complete the table by giving **two** finishing techniques that are suitable for use with each type of material.

Type of Material	Finishing Technique 1	Finishing Technique 2
Papers and boards		
Timber-based materials		
Metal-based materials		
Polymers		
Textile-based materials		

[10]

2 Which of the following describes the finishing process of galvanising? Tick the correct box.

a A powder is sprayed onto the metal and then it is heated. ☐

b Air is blown through a powder and then the metal is dipped and heated. ☐

c The metal is dipped into a bath of molten zinc. ☐

d An abrasive liquid is applied to the metal. ☐ [1]

3 What is the purpose of lubricating gears and mechanical parts?

....

.... [1]

Total Marks .... / 12

Selection of Materials

1 Choose **one** of the following products by circling your selection:

Food packaging   Flat-pack furniture   Electrical system in a fridge

    Plastic socket for an electric plug   Fabric covering for a sofa   Metal hammer

Discuss in detail the properties required by the product you have selected.

_____

_____

_____

_____

_____

_____

_____

_____

_____

_____

_____

_____

_____

_____

_____

[9]

Total Marks _____ / 9

Working with Materials

1 Explain why a designer may design a product that includes features to provide reinforcement.

....

....

....

....

....

....

....

....

[4]

2 Give **three** examples of different products that include reinforcement to add stiffness.

For each, identify the method of reinforcement used.

Product 1

....

....

....

Product 2

....

....

....

Product 1

....

....

....

[6]

Total Marks .... / 10

Scales of Manufacture

1 Explain how the scale of production affects the cost of a manufactured product.

[10]

Manufacturing Processes 1: Process Types and Processes used with Paper and Board

1 The product shown is A6 in size (folded from A5) and includes tear-off tags indicated by the dotted lines. The material available to make it is A1 sheets of duplex board.

1.1) Describe the processes that would be used to make a prototype batch of five of the products.

....

....

....

....

....

....

....

....

....

....

....

.... **[6]**

1.2) The final product will be made in batches of 10 000.

Identify a process that could be used to produce the net for the product in a single operation, so it only needs to be folded.

.... **[1]**

Total Marks .... / 7

Manufacturing Processes 2: Timber-Based Materials

1 Complete the table, identifying the tools that are typically used to carry out the tasks listed with timber-based materials.

Task	Tool that is Typically used to Carry Out this Task
Making a curved cut in a thin sheet of wood	a)
Hand smoothing the surface of a flat piece of timber before using abrasives	b)
Digging out waste material from a groove with sides at an angle of 60°	c)
Smoothing the surface of an irregularly shaped wooden part	d)
Turning a circular profile on a block of wood	e)
Removing large amounts of wood by hand when carving a shape	f)

[6]

2 Using notes and/or sketches, describe how laminating can be used to make a curved product from natural timber.

[4]

Total Marks .... / 10

Manufacturing Processes 3: Metals and Alloys

1 Describe the process of joining two metal parts using welding.

[6]

2 Explain how brazing is different to welding.

[4]

3 Name a metal joining technique that does not use heat.

[1]

Total Marks .... / 11

Manufacturing Processes 4: Polymers

1 Using notes and/or sketches, describe how a product is made using vacuum forming.

[10]

Total Marks _____ / 10

Manufacturing Processes 5: Textiles and Electronic Systems

1 **1.1)** Explain the difference between gathering and pleating.

....

....

.... [2]

1.2) Using notes and/or sketches, describe the process of batik.

[5]

2 Describe the process of reflow (flow) soldering.

....

....

....

....

....

.... [3]

Measurement and Production Aids

1 State what is meant by a 'datum surface' when measuring.

....

....

.... [2]

2 Explain **one** example of how each of the following tools can be used to ensure accuracy of manufacture of a product or part.

Jig

....

....

....

Pattern

....

....

....

.... [4]

Total Marks .... / 6

Ensuring Accuracy

1 Define the term 'accuracy'.

_____

_____

_____

_____

[2]

2 Explain what is meant by each of the following.

Quality control

_____

_____

_____

_____

Quality assurance

_____

_____

_____

_____

[4]

Total Marks _____ / 6

Impact on Industry

1 Explain **one** advantage and **one** disadvantage of increased automation in product manufacture.

Advantage

....

....

....

Disadvantage

....

....

.... [4]

2 State what is meant by 'crowd funding'.

....

....

....

.... [2]

3 Give an example of the use of virtual marketing.

....

.... [1]

Total Marks .... / 7

Impact on Production

1 Describe what is meant by 'lean manufacturing'.

....

....

....

....
[2]

2 Explain **one** advantage and **one** disadvantage of just-in-time production.

Advantage

....

....

....

Disadvantage

....

....

....
[4]

3 Describe the difference between market pull and technology push.

....

....

....

....
[2]

4 Give **two** examples of CAM equipment.

1 ....

2 ....
[2]

Total Marks .... / 10

Impact on Society and the Environment

1 This question is about the impact of new technologies on society and the environment.

Some elderly people have poor eyesight and therefore can have difficulty using telephones.

Give **two** ways that a telephone could be modified to help elderly people with poor eyesight.

1 ....

....

2 ....

....

[2]

2 Give **one** positive and **one** potentially negative impact of the increased use of smartphones on society.

Positive impact ....

....

Negative impact ....

....

[2]

3 Give **one** positive and **one** potentially negative impact of the increased use of smartphones on the environment.

Positive impact ....

....

Negative impact ....

....

[2]

Total Marks .... / 6

Collins

GCSE
Design and Technology

Time allowed: 2 hours

Materials

For this paper you must have:

- writing and drawing instruments
- a calculator
- a protractor.

Instructions

- Use black ink or ballpoint pen. Only use pencil for drawing.
- Answer all questions.
- Answer the questions in the spaces provided. Do not write on blank pages.
- Do all your rough work in this book and cross through any work that you do not want to be marked.

Information

- The marks for questions are shown in brackets.
- The maximum mark for this paper is 100.
- There are 20 marks for Section A, 30 marks for Section B and 50 marks for Section C.

Name: ....

Practice Exam Paper

Section A

Questions **1–10** are multiple choice questions. You must shade in one lozenge.

1   You have cut a piece of material to a measurement of 50 × 200 mm. The tolerance allowed is ±1 mm. Which of the following measurements is in tolerance?

    A 48.9 × 200.6 mm   ◯

    B 51.1 × 199.5 mm   ◯

    C 49.5 × 199.1 mm   ◯

    D 50.3 × 201.5 mm   ◯   **[1 mark]**

2   Which one of the following is a thermosetting polymer?

    A melamine formaldehyde   ◯

    B polypropylene   ◯

    C polyvinyl chloride   ◯

    D acrylic   ◯   **[1 mark]**

3 Which of the following properties means a material's resistance to abrasion, wear and scratches?

A absorbency ◯

B toughness ◯

C hardness ◯

D malleability ◯ **[1 mark]**

4 In a gear train similar to the one shown, the large gear has 36 teeth and the small gear has 12 teeth.

If the large gear turns at a rate of 30 revolutions per minute (rpm), what will be the rate of rotation of the small gear?

A 10 rpm ◯

B 30 rpm ◯

C 48 rpm ◯

D 90 rpm ◯ **[1 mark]**

5 An orthographic projection of a part has been drawn to a scale of 1:2. If the length of the part on the drawing is 20 mm, what is the length of the actual part?

A 10 mm ⭘

B 20 mm ⭘

C 30 mm ⭘

D 40 mm ⭘   **[1 mark]**

6 Which one of the following is a renewable energy source?

A wind ⭘

B coal ⭘

C gas ⭘

D nuclear ⭘   **[1 mark]**

7 Products are sometimes designed as a result of market forces. What is this known as?

A Efficient working ⭘

B Market pull ⭘

C Quality control ⭘

D Technology push ⭘   **[1 mark]**

8 Which of the following statements best describes the term 'fair trade'?

A   A business jointly owned and run by its members ◯

B   A method of marketing and selling a product ◯

C   A method of raising funding and awareness for a project ◯

D   A way of ensuring producers of products get a fair deal ◯   **[1 mark]**

9 A company has designed a product to fail within 5 years. What is this called?

A   Crowd funding ◯

B   Planned obsolescence ◯

C   Quality assurance ◯

D   Virtual marketing ◯   **[1 mark]**

1 0 Which of the following is the use of computers to support designing?

A   CAD ◯

B   CAM ◯

C   FMS ◯

D   JIT ◯   **[1 mark]**

Practice Exam Paper

1 1 · **1** Name a smart material.

_____

[1 mark]

1 1 · **2** Describe the smart property of this material.

_____

_____

_____

_____

[2 marks]

1 1 · **3** Give a typical application for this material.

_____

_____

[1 mark]

1 2 State the stage in an electronic system where each of the following would usually be found.

1 2 · **1** A buzzer making a sound

_____

[1 mark]

1 2 · **2** A sensor detecting a change in light level

_____

[1 mark]

1 3 Give **two** disadvantages of using non-renewable energy sources.

....

....

....

[2 marks]

1 4 Give **two** advantages of selecting rechargeable batteries instead of non-rechargeable batteries to power products.

....

....

....

[2 marks]

Practice Exam Paper

Section B

1 5 The following shape needs to be marked out on a piece of material for cutting.

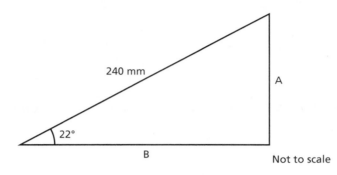

Figure 1

Calculate the length of side A.

_____

_____

_____

_____

[2 marks]

1 6 Choose **one** of the following products. Circle your choice.

Food packaging   Flat-pack furniture   Dessert spoon

Outdoor seat   Wedding dress

1 6 · 1 Identify **one** specific material that would be suitable for making the product that you have selected.

_____

[1 mark]

1 6 · 2 Explain why this material would be suitable.

[4 marks]

1 6 · 3 Identify a process that would be suitable for manufacturing your chosen product.

[1 mark]

1 6 · 4 Describe how this process would be used to manufacture the product.

[5 marks]

1 7 The shape shown needs to be cut out of a sheet of material using nesting to ensure that minimal material is wasted. The measurements are in millimetres. The sheet is 900 mm long by 900 mm wide.

Note: two of these shapes can be nested together to make a simple geometric shape.

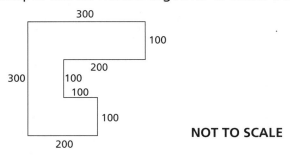

NOT TO SCALE

Figure 2

1 7 · 1 Repeat the shape on the grid to ensure that as many fit on the sheet as possible.

Each box on the grid represents a 100 × 100 mm size.

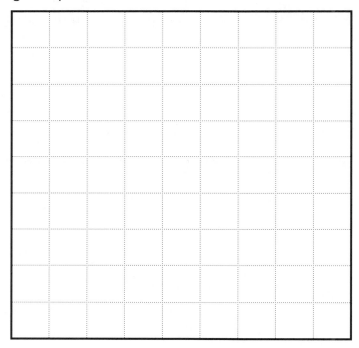

[2 marks]

`1` `7` · `2` Calculate the surface area of one shape.

[1 mark]

`1` `7` · `3` Calculate the percentage of material wasted when producing the shapes you have drawn above.

[4 marks]

1 8 There are several factors that must be considered when designing and manufacturing products and systems.

Discuss the importance of taking ecological issues into account when designing and manufacturing products and systems.

....

....

....

....

....

....

....

....

....

....

....

....

....

....

[10 marks]

Section C

The product shown is a pair of headphones for listening to music. They are to be worn while exercising. The target market is middle-aged adults.

1 9 . 1 State **four** factors that should be considered when evaluating the headphones.

....

....

....

....

[4 marks]

1 9 . 2 Evaluate the headphones against **three** of these factors.

1 ....

....

....

....

....

....

[4 marks]

2 ....

....

....

....

....

....

[4 marks]

3 ....

....

....

....

....

....

[4 marks]

2 0 The headphones shown on page 53 are to be redesigned for use by children aged 6–8 years. They should be suitable for use during a range of different play and learning activities.

2 0 · 1 Write a **four**-point design specification for the new product. For each point, explain its importance.

1 ....

....

....

[2 marks]

2 ....

....

....

[2 marks]

3 ....

....

....

[2 marks]

4 ....

....

....

[2 marks]

Practice Exam Paper

2 0 · 2 The designer of the new headphones has decided to look at the work of other designers before sketching a design idea.

Give the name of **two** different designers. For each, explain how their work could influence the design.

1 ....

....

....

....

[2 marks]

2 ....

....

....

....

[2 marks]

2 1 An iterative process was used to design the headphones shown on page 53.

2 1 · 1 Describe the iterative design process.

1 ....

....

....

....

....

....

[4 marks]

2 1 · 2 Discuss the advantages and disadvantages of using an iterative process to design products.

....

....

....

....

....

....

....

....

....

[6 marks]

Practice Exam Paper

2 2 Tolerances were considered when manufacturing the headphones.

2 2 . 1 What are tolerances?

_____

_____

_____

[2 marks]

2 2 . 2 Explain why tolerances are used in product manufacture.

_____

_____

_____

_____

_____

_____

[4 marks]

2 3 A group of 80 customers was asked to identify the most important characteristic in a new product. Their responses are given in the table.

Response	Number of Customers	Percentage of Total
Cost	36	45
Colour		25
Surface texture	8	
Weight	4	5
Undecided/no preference	12	15
Total	**80**	**100**

2 3 · 1 Insert the missing values in the table. **[2 marks]**

2 3 · 2 Use the information in the table to create a bar chart showing the number of customers who like different features. Label your axis with the scale of your graph.

[2 marks]

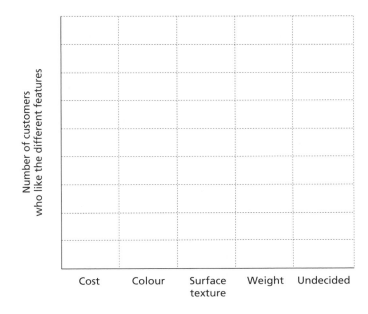

Cost   Colour   Surface texture   Weight   Undecided

2 3 . 3 Give **two** types of data that can be used when investigating user needs for products.

....

....

[2 marks]

END OF QUESTIONS

Answers

Page 4 Design Strategies

1. 1 mark for each suitable response. For example:

Design Approach	Advantage of Strategy	Disadvantage of Strategy
Iterative design	Problems with the design can be discovered and dealt with earlier [1].	It can be time consuming if a lot of prototypes or iterations need to be produced [1].
User-centred design	The end user has a greater ownership of the final product [1].	The design could become too focused on one particular end user's requirements [1].
Systems thinking	It is easier to find errors or faults in the design [1].	It can lead to the use of components that are not necessary [1].

Page 5 Electronic Systems

1. 1 mark for stating whether each component is an input, process or output and 1 mark for suitable application of each. For example:

Component	Input or Output	Application
Push switch	Input [1]	Starting the timing sequence on a kitchen timer [1]
Lamp	Output [1]	Providing light for a bicycle safety light [1].
Microcontroller	Process [1]	Controlling the counting sequence for the score counter on a board game [1]
Thermistor	Input [1]	Temperature sensor for an automatic heating system [1]
Buzzer	Output [1]	Making a buzzing sound for a doorbell [1]

Page 6 The Work of Others: Designers

1. 1 mark for any suitable named designer from the specification. For example: Coco Chanel [1].
2. 1 mark for product designed by designer given in answer to question 1. For example: Chanel Suit [1].
3. 1 mark for each suitable feature of design given in answer to question 2. For example: Chanel suit: masculine/bold look [1], three-piece sleeve [1], machine-quilted lining on jacket [1], made with soft/flexible materials [1].

Page 7 The Work of Others: Companies

1. 1 mark for any suitable named design company from the specification. For example: Under Armour [1].
2. 1 mark for product designed by company given in answer to question 1. For example: moisture-wicking t-shirt [1].
3. 1 mark for each suitable feature of design given in answer to question 2. For example: moisture-wicking t-shirt: keeps athlete cool [1], removes sweat from body [1], lightweight [1], made using microfibres [1].

Page 8 Ecological, Environmental and Social Issues

1. Up to 2 marks for explanation of each way. For example: choose recyclable materials [1] so that less new material needs to be sourced [1]. Design for disassembly [1] so that materials/components can be reused [1]. Select a sustainable power supply [1] to reduce reliance on non-renewable energy [1].
2. Up to 2 marks for definition. For example: fair trade is a movement that works to help people in developing countries [1] to get a fair deal for the products that they produce [1].

Page 9 Research and Investigation

1. Up to 2 marks for explanation. For example: to find out if there is a gap in the market [1] so that a product will be commercially successful [1].
2. Up to 2 marks for explanation. For example: to gain feedback from potential customers [1] to ensure that the product will meet their needs [1].
3. 1 mark for each correct type of data. For example: primary data [1]; secondary data [1].
4. 1 mark for correct answer: b

Page 10 Briefs and Specifications

1. 1 mark for each specification point and 1 mark for explanation for each. Specification may relate to any suitable product that matches the brief. For example:
   • The product must use bright and attractive colours [1] so it would appeal aesthetically to the child [1].
   • The product must have no sharp edges [1] so as not to cause injury to the child [1].
   • The product must have a set of lettered blocks [1] so that the child can practise making different words [1].

Page 11 Exploring and Developing Ideas

1. 1 mark for each suitable stage given. For example: modelling [1], testing [1], evaluating [1], improving/refining outcome [1].
2. 1 mark for each reason or 2 marks for each reason explained further, up to a maximum of 4 marks. For example: to get ideas onto paper very quickly [1] as freehand sketches do not have to follow drawing conventions [1]. To share early ideas with potential clients [1] so that they can provide feedback [1].

Page 12 Communication of Ideas 1

1. 1.1) Award 1 mark or each of the following:
   • Design appears to be in correct proportion/to scale.
   • Vertical lines/leading edges go straight up.
   • Correct use of guidelines for the horizontal lines.
   • Design is clearly visible as some form of toy car.
   1.2) Award marks up to a maximum of 6 marks as follows:
   • 1 mark each for two sizes
   • 1 mark each for two materials or one material and one finish; or 2 marks for a material with an explanation of why it is suggested
   • 1 mark each for two identified manufacturing processes; or 2 marks for a manufacturing process with an explanation of why it is suggested.

Page 13 Communication of Ideas 2

1. Award 1 mark for each of the following, up to a maximum of 11 marks:
   • layout includes three views (top, front, side)
   • top view is accurate representation
   • front view is accurate representation
   • side view is accurate representation
   • views are laid out in correct orientation (top above; front below; side to the right of the front)

- views are aligned with each other
- one to four dimensions listed [1]; all five dimensions listed [2]
- leader lines are shown to dimensions
- dimension lines are finished with solid arrowheads
- dimensions are located above the line in the centre (or horizontal measurements) or to the left of the line and in the centre (for vertical measurements).

Not to scale

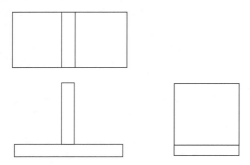

Page 14 Computer-Based Tools

1. 1 mark for each correct answer – also accept specific items of software if given.

Task	Computer-Based Tool
Creating a bill of materials for a product that is to be manufactured	Spreadsheet software
Creating a 3D model of a product	CAD software
Preparing images of a product prototype for inclusion in a face-to-face presentation	Image-manipulation software
Creating visual aids for presentation of a prototype at a focus group meeting	Presentation software
Hosting a virtual meeting	Video conferencing software

2. 2.1) Spreadsheet software [1]
   2.2) CAD [1]

Page 15 Prototype Development

1. 1 mark for each reason. For example: to assess if it is fit for purpose [1]. To identify modifications needed [1].
2. 1 mark for each consideration. For example: whether the product is marketable [1]; whether it functions correctly [1]; whether it is aesthetically pleasing [1]; whether it meets the needs of the brief/specification [1]; whether it meets the needs of the client [1]; whether it is innovative/creative [1].

Page 16 Energy Generation and Storage

1. 1 mark for stating whether each source of energy is renewable or non-renewable and up to 2 marks for suitable description of how each is used to produce energy. For example:

Source of Energy	Renewable of Non-Renewable	Description of How Energy is Produced
Nuclear power	Non-renewable [1]	A nuclear reactor creates steam [1] which is used to turn turbines [1]. *Note: reference must be made to nuclear reactor or nuclear reaction producing steam to gain 1 mark.*
Solar energy	Renewable [1]	Solar panels collect light from the sun [1] and convert it into an electric current [1].
Wind energy	Renewable [1]	The wind turns turbines [1] which then drive generators to produce electricity [1].

Page 17 Mechanical Systems 1

1. 1.1) Oscillating [1]
   1.2) Linear [1]
   1.3) Rotating [1]
   1.4) Reciprocating [1]
2. Mechanical advantage = load / effort [1] = 60 / 24 = 2.5 [1]
   For a first-class lever, mechanical advantage = A / 60
   Rearranging A = mechanical advantage × 60 [1] = 2.5 × 60 = 150 mm [1]

Page 18 Mechanical Systems 2

1. Award marks, up to a maximum of 4 marks, as follows: a follower can only rise (go up), dwell (be held at the same height) or fall (go down) [1]. How long the follower spends doing each of these depends on the shape of the cam [1]. A round section on the cam will provide a dwell [1]. The longer the round section, the longer the dwell [1]. A snail cam (or similar) will provide a sudden drop [1]. Any other relevant point.
2. Gear ratio needed = speed of output gear / speed of input gear [1] = 240 / 60 = 4:1 [1]
   Number of teeth needed = number of teeth on input gear / gear ratio [1] = 48 / 4 = 12 [1]

Page 19 Properties of Materials

1. 1.1) The ability of a material not to break when a force is applied to it suddenly [1]
   1.2) The ability of electricity to pass through a material [1]
   1.3) The ability of a material to return to its original shape when a force is removed [1]
2. 2.1) Malleability [1]
   2.2) Fusibility [1]
   2.3) Absorbency [1]
3. A physical property is a measurable characteristic of the material itself [1] whereas a working property is a reaction to some form of applied force [1].

Page 20 Materials: Paper and Board

1. Award up to 4 marks as follows. For example: solid white board is made from pure bleached wood pulp [1] and is white all the way through [1]. Duplex board has white surfaces with grey fibres in between [1] and costs less than solid white board [1]. It also has slightly less strength [1]. The available sizes of duplex board are typically slightly thicker than solid white board [1].
2. Award 1 mark for an attempt to tessellate that is inefficient. Award 2 marks for effective tessellation, for example:

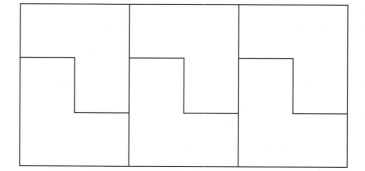

Page 21 Materials: Timber

1. a) Softwood [1]
   b) Any suitable application. For example: boats and yachts, exterior cladding of buildings, interior panelling [1].
   c) Hardwood [1]
   d) Any suitable application. For example: high-quality furniture [1].
   e) Manufactured board [1]
   f) Any suitable application. For example: furniture, boat building [1].
   g) Softwood [1]
   h) Any suitable application. For example: general construction, wooden aircraft frames [1].
   i) Hardwood [1]
   j) Any suitable application. For example: modelling [1].
2. Seasoning means that the wood is dried before use to remove moisture [1], either in air or by gentle heating in a large kiln [1]. This makes the wood less likely to distort or warp [1].

Page 22 Materials: Metals

1. 1.1) Award 1 mark each for iron and chromium.
   1.2) Award 1 mark each for copper and zinc.
2. 2.1) Award 1 mark each for up to four of the following: sheet, plate, round bar, square bar, square tube and round tube.
   2.2) Award marks as indicated, up to a maximum of 4 marks. For example: to reform metal it requires much energy [1] and effort [1], and therefore cost [1]. By using a stock form, this cost can be avoided [1].
3. Ferrous metals contain iron; non-ferrous ones do not [1].

Page 23 Materials: Polymers

1. Award marks as indicated, up to a maximum of 4 marks, for notes or sketches communicating the following content: oil is extracted [1]; this is sent to an industrial refinery [1]; small chemical units called monomers are extracted from the oil [1], which are linked together to form the polymer chains in the polymerisation process [1]. This material can then be extruded/rolled/granulated into the required form [1].
2. Volume of 1 cube = 0.03^3 [1] = 2.7×10^{-5} m³ [1]
   Volume of 10 000 cubes = $2.7 \times 10^{-5} \times 10000 = 0.27$ m³ [1]
   Mass of 10 000 cubes = 0.27×960 [1] = 259.2 kg [1]

Page 24 Materials: Textiles

1. 1.1) Award 1 mark for cotton, wool or silk.
   1.2) Award 1 mark for a suitable application. For example: underwear, shirts and blouses, t-shirts or jeans for cotton; jumpers, suits, dresses or carpets for wool; dresses, shirts or ties for silk.
   1.3) Award 1 mark each for up to three properties that make it suitable for the stated application. For example: strong, durable, absorbent for cotton; warm, soft, absorbent, crease resistant for wool; smooth, lustrous and strong for silk.
2. 2.1) Award 1 mark for polyamide/nylon, polyester or elastane/lycra.
   2.2) Award 1 mark for a suitable application. For example: tights and stockings, sportswear, upholstery, carpets for nylon; sportswear for polyester; sportswear, underwear, socks, suits for elastane.
   2.3) Award 1 mark each for up to three properties that make it suitable for the stated application. For example: strong, durable, warm or crease resistant for nylon; strong, durable, elastic, or crease resistant for polyester; high extension and elasticity/stretch for elastane.

Page 25 New Materials

1. 1.1) A material that has a property that changes in response to its environment [1]. This change is reversible [1].
   1.2) Award 1 mark for naming a suitable material, such as: shape memory alloy, thermochromic pigment, photochromic pigment.
   1.3) Award 1 mark for stating the property of the material and a second mark for stating the environmental stimulus to which it responds. For example: shape memory alloy reverts to its original shape [1] when heat is applied [1]; thermochromic pigment changes colour [1] in response to temperature [1]; photochromic pigment becomes darker/changes colour [1] in response to increased brightness [1].
   1.4) Award 1 mark for naming a suitable application. For example: shape memory alloy: spectacle frames, fire detectors; thermochromic pigment: flexible thermometers, food packaging; photochromic pigment: sunglasses.
2. 2.1) A textile manufactured for performance properties rather than visual appearance [1]
   2.2) Award 1 mark for identifying the technical textile and 1 mark for the application. For example: Kevlar [1] for body armour [1]; fire-resistant fibre [1] used in clothing worn by firefighters [1]; microfibres incorporating micro-encapsulation [1] used for socks and underwear that reduce body odour, or anti-bacterial medical textiles [1]; conductive fibres [1] used to integrate temperature controlled clothing or to integrate lights into emergency clothing [1].

Page 26 Standard Components

1. 1.1) Award 1 mark each for any two, e.g. fasteners, seals, bindings.
   1.2) Award 1 mark each for any two, e.g. zips, press studs, velcro, buttons and poppers, decorative items.
   1.3) Award 1 mark each for any two, e.g. nuts and bolts, machine screws, rivets, hinges and washers.
   1.4) Award 1 mark each for any two, e.g. woodscrews, hinges, knock-down fittings.
2. Award marks as indicated, up to a maximum of 4 marks. For example: making components in small quantities can be very expensive [1] due to the labour time [1] and equipment required [1]. It normally costs less to buy standard components [1] and they can offer more consistent quality [1]. Any other relevant point.

Page 27 Finishing Materials

1. 1 mark for each suitable finishing technique for each material. For example:

Type of Material	Finishing Technique 1	Finishing Technique 2
Papers and boards	UV varnishing [1]	Embossing [1]
Timber-based materials	Varnishing [1]	Tanalising [1]
Metal-based materials	Dip-coating [1]	Galvanising [1]
Polymers	Polishing [1]	Vinyl decals [1]
Textile-based materials	Block printing [1]	Screen printing [1]

2. 1 mark for the correct answer: c
3. It reduces the effects of friction [1].

Page 28 Selection of Materials

1. 7–9 marks: thorough knowledge and understanding of the properties required, with a minimum of five properties considered. Explanations are given for why all the identified properties are needed. 4–6 marks: good knowledge and understanding of the properties required, with a minimum of three properties considered. Explanation included for why some of the identified properties are needed. 1–3 marks:

limited knowledge or understanding. Mainly descriptive response, stating a few of the properties required.

Properties specific to the application that could be considered include the following.

Food packaging	• Absorbency, to prevent spoilage of contents or damage to the packaging • Ability to be printed, to give aesthetic appeal • Cost
Flat-pack furniture	• Toughness, to resist impacts • Hardness, to resist being scratched or damaged in use • Cost
Metal hammer	• Strength • Toughness, to resist impact if hit or dropped • Malleability, ability to be made into the shape of the tool (as material is very hard and may be difficult to form)
Plastic socket for an electric plug	• Electrical conductivity: it should be an insulator to protect the user from the electrical circuit inside it • Toughness, so that it doesn't break if accidentally knocked, causing safety issues
Fabric covering for a sofa	• Aesthetics: colour and texture that appeal to the user • Hardwearing so it lasts a long time • Non-flammable, so that it does not burn
Electrical system in a fridge	• Absorbency and resistance to corrosion, so that it is not damaged by the materials, water or food that contact it in use • Strength, to support whatever is put into it and to resist damage if someone sits on it! • Electrical conductivity: it should insulate the circuitry to prevent electric shocks to the user

In addition, general properties considered (in addition to the above list, where not duplicated) could include: functionality, aesthetics, environmental considerations, availability of materials, cost, social factors, ethical considerations and cultural factors.

Page 29 Working with Materials

1. Award 1 mark each for up to four of the following: To achieve the properties needed in an application [1]. It costs less to reinforce just the area where enhanced properties are needed [1], rather than using a thicker material for the whole design [1] (which would also weigh more [1]) or a more expensive material with superior properties [1].
2. Award 1 mark for each suitable example and a further mark for correctly identifying the method of reinforcement. For example: battery holders [1] with webbing and internal ribs [1]; shirt collars [1] including interfacing [1]; disposable food trays [1] with bent (and sometimes folded) edges [1].

Page 30 Scales of Manufacture

1. Award up to 10 marks as follows: one-off/bespoke production leads to the highest cost per product [1] as it requires the most labour time per product [1] and this labour is provided by highly skilled craftsmen [1]. Batch production groups identical products together which means that there is less non-making time due to equipment changeovers [1]. Dedicated jigs may be used to speed up production on some processes [1]. Some processes may be automated, speeding up production [1], as the cost can be divided between the quantity of products made [1]. Mass and continuous production lead to the lowest cost per product [1] when large

quantities of products are made [1]. Tools and equipment are dedicated to making one product [1], which means no time is lost to changing between products [1] and the high cost of the equipment can be divided between all of the products made [1]. Dedicated jigs and fixtures will be used [1] and most processes will be automated [1], speeding up production [1]. Labour costs are typically lower [1], as some lower-skill workers are used for production-line roles [1]. Any other relevant point.

Page 31 Manufacturing Processes 1: Process Types and Processes used with Paper and Board

1. 1.1) Award up to 6 marks as follows: the sheet would need to be marked out [1], then cut using a rotary trimmer or guillotine [1]. The perforations for the tear-off tags [1] could be made using a perforation cutter [1]. The fold could be *either* manually scored [1], for example using scissors [1], and then folded *or* creased [1] with a creasing bar [1] then folded.
   1.2) Die cutting [1].

Page 32 Manufacturing Processes 2: Timber-Based Materials

1. a) Any one of: coping saw, powered fretsaw, jigsaw and band saw [1]
   b) Smoothing plane [1]
   c) Bevel-edged chisel; also accept firmer chisel but not just 'chisel' [1]
   d) Sandpaper; also accept belt, disc or bobbin sander [1]
   e) Wood lathe [1]
   f) Rasp or surform; also accept gouge chisel [1]
2. Award up to 4 marks as follows (information can be in either sketches or notes): thin sheets of the timber [1] are glued together using PVA [1]. These are shaped round a former while the glue is wet [1] and clamped in place until the glue dries [1] when it will retain the shape of the former [1].

Page 33 Manufacturing Processes 3: Metals and Alloys

1. Award marks as indicated up to a maximum of 6 marks: the parts to be joined are cleaned [1] and any oxide, rust or grease is removed [1]. They are placed together to form the joint [1]. A heat source from a flame/electric arc is applied [1]. This melts the edges of the parts so they join together [1]. A filler wire may be used [1] especially if there is a gap between the parts being joined [1]. The joint is then allowed to cool [1] and cleaned/descaled if necessary [1].
2. Award marks as indicated up to a maximum of 4 marks: brazing is carried out at a lower temperature than welding [1]. The parts to be joined do not melt [1]. A filler metal must be used; in welding this is sometimes not needed [1]. The joint is a different alloy to the parent metal [1]. A brazed joint is not normally as strong as a welded joint [1]. Any other relevant point.
3. Award 1 mark for either epoxy resin or riveting.

Page 34 Manufacturing Processes 4: Polymers

1. Award marks as follows up to a maximum of 10 marks (information can be in either sketches or notes): a mould is made [1], the mould is placed inside the vacuum-forming machine [1], a sheet of material is clamped across the top [1], the material must be a thermoforming polymer [1], the material is heated until it softens [1], the mould is raised [1], a vacuum is applied to suck out the air between the mould and the plastic [1], air pressure from the atmosphere pushes the plastic against the mould [1], air may be blown in to help the mould release from the product [1], the mould is lowered and the plastic sheet is unclamped [1], the product is cut out of the plastic sheet [1].

Page 35 Manufacturing Processes 5: Textiles and Electronic Systems

1. **1.1)** In pleating the folds are larger [1] and stitching may be at either the top or side [1].
   1.2) Award up to 5 marks as follows (information can be in either sketches or notes):
   wax is applied to the surface of the cloth [1], either by drawing the design with a spouted tool called a canting [1] or by printing with a copper stamp called a cap [1]. The cloth is then soaked in a dye [1]. Areas with the applied wax resist the dye and remain uncoloured [1]. The wax can then be removed with boiling water [1].
2. Solder paste is applied to a PCB [1] and the components positioned on their contact pads [1]. The whole assembly is then heated to melt the solder, creating the joint [1].

Page 36 Measurement and Production Aids

1. Up to 2 marks for correct answer. For example: a reference point [1] on a material/product/object [1].
2. Up to 2 marks for explanation of each example. For example:
   • Jig: holding and positioning a drill [1] to ensure that holes are drilled in the same place on two pieces of wood [1].
   • Pattern: providing a pattern for a dress [1] so that the parts can be traced accurately onto fabric [1].

Page 37 Ensuring Accuracy

1. Up to 2 marks for correct definition. For example: the degree of closeness of a measurement [1] to its true value/correct value/standard [1].
2. Up to 2 marks for explanation of each example. For example:
   • Quality control is about testing and checking [1] that a product meets the specification/a set of defined quality standards [1].
   • Quality assurance is putting systems in place [1] that ensure the quality of the processes used to manufacture the product [1].

Page 38 Impact on Industry

1. Up to 2 marks each for explanation of advantage and disadvantage. For example:
   • Advantage: increased efficiency of manufacture [1] due to robots being able to work continuously [1].
   • Disadvantage: decreased employment opportunities [1] due to robots replacing people [1].
2. Up to 2 marks for definition. For example: a way for people to raise awareness and money for a project or idea [1], where people donate money in return for rewards [1].
3. 1 mark for suitable example. For example: email marketing to promote a product [1].

Page 39 Impact on Production

1. Up to 2 marks for description. For example: lean manufacturing is an approach that aims to make products in the most effective and efficient way possible [1] by eliminating all forms of waste during manufacturing [1].
2. Up to 2 marks each for explanation of advantage and disadvantage. For example:
   • Advantage: less storage space is needed [1] because suppliers deliver materials only when they are required [1].
   • Disadvantage : production may have to be stopped [1] if materials are not delivered by suppliers on time [1].
3. Up to 2 marks for description of difference. For example: technology push is when new products are produced because of new materials/manufacturing methods becoming available [1], whereas market pull is when new products are developed because of market forces [1].
4. Any two of: laser cutter [1], vinyl cutter [1], 3D plotter [1], any other suitable CAM equipment [1].

Page 40 Impact on Society and the Environment

1. 1 mark for each suitable improvement. For example: increase size of buttons [1], increase size of text on buttons/screen [1].
2. 1 mark for positive impact and 1 mark for negative impact. For example:
   • Positive impact: people can easily communicate with each other anytime/anywhere [1].
   • Negative impact: people can spend less time communicating face to face [1].
3. 1 mark for positive impact and 1 mark for negative impact. For example:
   • Positive impact: less pollution created from travelling [1].
   • Negative impact: increased electronic waste [1].

Pages 41–47 Practice Exam Paper Section A

1. C [1]
2. A [1]
3. C [1]
4. D [1]
5. D [1]
6. A [1]
7. B [1]
8. D [1]
9. B [1]
10. A [1]
11. **11.1)** Award 1 mark for a suitable material. For example: shape memory alloy, thermochromic pigment or photochromic pigment.
    11.2) Award 1 mark for stating the property and 1 mark for stating the stimuli that it responds to. For example: shape memory alloy returns to its original shape [1] when heated [1]; thermochromic pigment changes colour [1] with temperature [1]; photochromic pigment changes colour/gets darker [1] with increasing brightness [1].
    11.3) Award 1 mark for stating a suitable application. For example: shape memory alloy: spectacle frames; thermochromic pigment: food packaging; photochromic pigment: sunglasses.
12. **12.1)** Output
    12.2) Input
13. 1 mark for each suitable disadvantage given. For example: more carbon emissions, will eventually run out.
14. 1 mark for each suitable advantage given. For example: less waste produced, reduced cost of buying new batteries.

Pages 48–52 Practice Exam Paper Section B

15. A = 240 × sin 22° = 89.9 mm [1 mark for method, 1 mark for answer]
16. **16.1)** 1 mark for any suitable specific material. For example, polypropylene for outdoor seat. Material identified must be specific to gain a mark: plastic, wood, etc. should gain no marks.
    16.2) 3–4 marks: detailed response with at least two points explained further. 1–2 marks: one or two valid points presented but with little further explanation.
    For example: polypropylene is very strong [1] so could withstand applied forces without breaking [1]. Polypropylene is waterproof [1] so would not be damaged by rainfall [1].
    16.3) 1 mark for any suitable manufacturing process. For example: injection moulding for an outdoor seat.
    16.4) 1 mark for each suitable descriptive point up to a maximum of 5 marks. Points must be in the correct order for full marks. For example: injection moulding: plastic powder or granules are fed from a hopper into the machine [1]. Heaters melt the plastic as the screw moves it along towards the mould [1]. Once enough plastic has been melted, the screw forces the plastic into the mould [1]. Pressure is maintained on the mould [1] until it has cooled enough to be opened [1].

17. **17.1)** Award 1 mark for nesting two shapes together to form a 400 × 300 mm rectangle; award a further mark for nesting the shapes as follows:

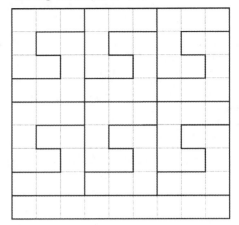

17.2) Area of one shape = 400 × 300 / 2 = 60,000 mm² (accept alternative methods) [1]

17.3) 1 mark for calculating the total area of the shapes (A). 1 mark for calculating the area of the sheet (B). 1 mark for calculating the amount of wasted material, C (B – A). 1 mark for calculating the percentage wasted = 1 – ((B – A) / B) × 100 / 1.
Calculations:
A = 12 × 60 000 = 720 000 mm² [1]
B = 900 × 900 = 810 000 mm² [1]
C = 810 000 – 720 000 = 90 000 mm² [1]
% = 90 000 / 810 000 × 100 / 1 = 11.1% [1]

18. 9–10 marks: balanced discussion that comes to a fully justified conclusion. All points discussed in detail. Excellent coverage. 7–8 marks: balanced discussion that comes to a conclusion, with some justification. Most points discussed in detail. Very good coverage. 5–6 marks: discussion with some balance. Some points discussed in detail. Good coverage. 3–4 marks: discussion lacks balance. Some points discussed, but may lack detail. Some coverage. 1–2 marks: mainly descriptive response with little discussion. Limited coverage.

Indicative answer: answer should discuss around the following points. For example: deforestation caused by use of timber-based materials: loss of habitats; drilling for oil for plastics/ mining for metal ore: impact on local ecosystem; farming for biomaterials: use of pesticides that can kill other animals; mileage of product throughout venture life cycle: cause of pollution; production of carbon from manufacturing products: impact on global warming.

Pages 53–60 Practice Exam Paper Section C

19. **19.1)** 1 mark for each suitable consideration. For example: aesthetics [1], ergonomics [1], function [1], usability [1].

19.2) For each factor: 3–4 marks: detailed evaluation with fully justified conclusions; 1–2 marks: limited evaluation. Some conclusions drawn but may not be justified.
For example: ergonomics: the headphones have padded ear muffs, which would make them comfortable to wear. The ear muffs are adjustable, so they can be moved to fit the correct size of head.

20. **20.1)** 1 mark for each valid specification point and 1 mark for each supporting explanation. For example: the product must have images on the ear pieces [1] so it would be visually appealing to the child [1]. The product must have a fully adjustable headpiece [1] to accommodate the child growing [1]. The product must be simple to use [1] so it is accessible to the child [1]. The product must be made from durable materials [1] so it is not easily broken by the child [1].

20.2) 1 mark for each designer and 1 mark for each explanation of influence. For example: Gerrit Rietveld [1]: use of only black, white and primary colours in the design [1]. Norman Foster [1]: use of latest technologies to improve the function of the product [1].

21. **21.1)** 1 mark for each valid descriptive point up to a maximum of 4 marks. A model is produced [1]. The model is tested/evaluated [1]. Changes/refinements are made [1], leading to a new iteration [1].

21.2) 5–6 marks: detailed, balanced discussion that comes to a fully justified conclusion. 3–4 marks: discussion with some detail but may focus overly on advantages or disadvantages. Comes to a conclusion but this may not be justified. 1–2 marks: mainly descriptive response. No conclusion.

Indicative answer: each iteration is fully tested and evaluated, so it is more likely that problems with the design will be discovered earlier. User feedback is constantly being gathered, which helps to ensure the design meets their needs. However, designers can become so focused on the current iteration that they sometimes lose sight of the bigger design picture. It can also be time consuming if a lot of prototypes or iterations need to be produced.

22. **22.1)** 1 mark for each suitable point. For example: the permissible limits of variation [1] in the dimensions of a manufactured product [1].

22.2) 1 mark for each suitable point up to a maximum of 4 marks. For example: so that manufacturers understand the importance of the dimensions/measurements that they have been given [1]. Failure to consider tolerances can lead to improper fits [1], wasted materials [1] and the additional cost of remaking a product [1].

23. **23.1)** 20 [1], 10% [1]

23.2) Award 1 mark for correct scaling. Award 1 mark for accurate drawing of the graph.

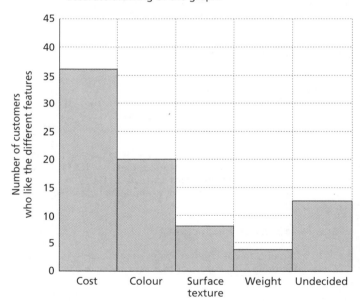

23.3) 1 mark for each type: primary [1], secondary [1].

Notes

Notes

Notes

Notes

Rethink Revision

Have you ever taken part in a quiz and thought '*I know this*!', but, despite frantically racking your brain, you just couldn't come up with the answer?

It's very frustrating when this happens, but in a fun situation it doesn't really matter. However, in your GCSE exams, it will be essential that you can recall the relevant information quickly when you need to.

Most students think that revision is about making sure you **know** stuff. Of course, this is important, but it is also about becoming confident that you can **retain** that *stuff* over time and **recall** it quickly when needed.

Revision That Really Works

Experts have discovered that there are two techniques that help with all of these things and consistently produce better results in exams compared to other revision techniques.

Applying these techniques to your GCSE revision will ensure you get better results in your exams and will have all the relevant knowledge at your fingertips when you start studying for further qualifications, like AS and A Levels, or begin work.

It really isn't rocket science either – you simply need to:

- **test yourself** on each topic as many times as possible
- **leave a gap** between the test sessions.

It is most effective if you leave a good period of time between the test sessions, e.g. between a week and a month. The idea is that just as you start to forget the information, you force yourself to recall it again, keeping it fresh in your mind.

Three Essential Revision Tips

1. **Use Your Time Wisely**
   - Allow yourself plenty of time.
   - Try to start revising six months before your exams – it's more effective and less stressful.
   - Your revision time is precious so use it wisely – using the techniques described on this page will ensure you revise effectively and efficiently and get the best results.
   - Don't waste time re-reading the same information over and over again – it's time-consuming and not effective!

2. **Make a Plan**
   - Identify all the topics you need to revise.
   - Plan at least five sessions for each topic.
   - One hour should be ample time to test yourself on the key ideas for a topic.
   - Spread out the practice sessions for each topic – the optimum time to leave between each session is about one month but, if this isn't possible, just make the gaps as big as realistically possible.

3. **Test Yourself**
   - Methods for testing yourself include: quizzes, practice questions, flashcards, past papers, explaining a topic to someone else, etc.
   - Don't worry if you get an answer wrong – provided you check what the correct answer is, you are more likely to get the same or similar questions right in future!

Visit our website for more information about the benefits of these revision techniques and for further guidance on how to plan ahead and make them work for you.

www.collins.co.uk/collinsGCSErevision

Acknowledgements

The author and publisher are grateful to the copyright holders for permission to use quoted materials and images.

Cover © violetblue/Shutterstock.com
All other images © Shutterstock.com

Every effort has been made to trace copyright holders and obtain their permission for the use of copyright material. The author and publisher will gladly receive information enabling them to rectify any error or omission in subsequent editions. All facts are correct at time of going to press.

Published by Collins
An imprint of HarperCollins*Publishers* Ltd
1 London Bridge Street
London SE1 9GF

© HarperCollins*Publishers* Limited 2017

ISBN 9780008326807

Content first published 2017
This edition published 2018

10 9 8 7 6 5 4 3 2 1

British Library Cataloguing in Publication Data.

A CIP record of this book is available from the British Library.

Authored by: Paul Anderson and David Hills-Taylor
Project management and editorial: Nik Prowse
Commissioning: Katherine Wilkinson and Katie Galloway
Cover Design: Sarah Duxbury and Paul Oates
Inside Concept Design: Sarah Duxbury and Paul Oates
Text Design and Layout: Jouve India Private Limited
Production: Lyndsey Rogers
Printed in the UK, by Martins The Printers

Collins AQA GCSE 9-1 Revision

With topic-based questions and a practice exam paper in one book, this AQA GCSE 9-1 Design and Technology Workbook contains plenty of practice opportunities to ensure the best results.

Answers included

Topic-by-topic practice

When it comes to revision, research has proved that **repeated practice testing** is more effective than **repeated study**, and for best effect the practice should be spaced out over time.

This workbook reflects these principles so that you can be confident of achieving the best results possible.

For more information visit www.collins.co.uk/collinsGCSErevision

Collins
FREEDOM TO TEACH
Find us at www.collins.co.uk
and follow our blog – articles and information by teachers for teachers.
@FreedomToTeach
facebook.com/CollinsSecondary

ISBN 978-0-00-832680-7

9 780008 326807

£5.99